Doll & Teddy Bear
Activity Book

Pune Dracker

Reverie
PUBLISHING COMPANY

First edition/First printing

Text on pages 33–36 and 41–44 copyright © 2005 Krystyna Poray Goddu.

Paper doll on pages 38–39 copyright © 2005 Ginnie Hofmann.

Paper doll on pages 46–47 copyright © 2005 Kathleen Bart.

Photos on pages 33–36: 1, 4–9, 11–14 courtesy Theriault's, Annapolis, MD;
2 & 10 courtesy Walter Pfeiffer; 3 courtesy Sotheby's.

Photos on pages 41–44: 1 & 8 courtesy Doris and Terry Michaud;
2 courtesy Dee Hockenberry; 3 & 4 courtesy Walter Pfeiffer;
5–7 courtesy Evelyn and Mort Wood Collection; 9 courtesy Don and Helen Marlowe.

Activities on pages 7, 20, 49, 74 & 80 by Michael Shtadtlender.

Activities on pages 9, 28–29, 76 & 79 by Brent Pallas.

Drawings on pages 22–23 & 26 by Nancy Lane.

Bearigami on pages 68–69 by Gregory Bellafiore.

To purchase additional copies of this book, please contact:
Reverie Publishing Company, 130 South Wineow Street, Cumberland, MD 21502.
888-721-4999. www.reveriepublishing.com

ISBN: 1-932485-24-4

Cover illustrations: Ginnie Hofmann (front and back) and Kathleen Bart (front)
Jacket design: Anna Christian
Interior design and production: Anna Christian

Printed and bound in Korea

Introduction

This book is filled with games, puzzles, projects and stories about dolls and teddy bears. We're guessing that if you are reading this, you like dolls and teddy bears. Well, you have very good taste—and you're in good company, too! Children have been playing with dolls for centuries, and they've been cuddling with teddies for just a little more than 100 years. We've tried hard to make sure that you will have tons of fun with the word searches, mazes, crossword puzzles, silly stories and paper dolls (and paper teddies!) in this book. You also may learn some interesting history and facts about these favorite toys along the way. Ever wonder why the teddy bear is called a "teddy" bear? Or who came up with the idea of the Barbie doll? The answers are all somewhere in this book!

Before you begin you might want to read "Hello, Dolly!" on pages 33–36 and "Can You Imagine a World Without Teddy Bears?" on pages 41–44. The answers to some of the activities can be found in those stories. We also strongly suggest you use a pencil, not a pen or a marker, to do the activities . . . just in case you decide to change an answer. And finally—don't be afraid to ask a friend or older relative to try some of the harder activities with you. We've included challenges for all ages! (When you're done, check pages 92–96 for the answers.)

Sharpen your pencils, put on your thinking caps, grab your favorite teddy or doll (or both!) for inspiration, and . . . HAVE FUN!

Go'wn Around

Can you find your way out of this mess—or should we say dress?!

Rhyme Time

Got a few minutes to *spare*? Then grab a *chair* and give it a try—if you *dare*!

Hidden in the puzzle below are 10 words that rhyme with the word BEAR.

AIR	BEWARE	CHAIR
DARE	FAIR	HARE	PEAR
PRAYER	SPARE	TEAR

```
R  E  Y  A  R  P  F
T  S  O  W  E  E  A
E  P  Y  A  R  R  I
A  A  R  A  I  A  R
R  R  W  S  A  D  U
P  E  R  A  H  O  G
B  A  I  R  C  X  I
```

What's in a Word?

How many words of three letters or more can you find in the words Teddy Bear? You can write your answers on the lines below. (If you run out of lines, use another sheet of paper.) People's names and proper nouns don't count. Good luck!

TEDDY BEAR

_____   _____
_____   _____
_____   _____
_____   _____
_____   _____
_____   _____
_____   _____
_____   _____
_____   _____
_____   _____
_____   _____
_____   _____
_____   _____
_____   _____

IF YOU FOUND...

1 to 10 words: You're off to a good start, but you're still a cub! Keep trying, and soon you'll be ready for a hike in the forest.

11 to 30 words: Congratulations, you're on your way. Looks like they put some "smarts" in your stuffing!

31 to 50 words: Now you're really on a roll! Can we shake your paw?

51+ words: You're a rare bear indeed! Grab that jar of honey and have yourself a well-deserved reward.

Find the Twins

Can you figure out which two dolls are exactly the same?

Quick Change

How do you turn a doll into a bear—and back again?

By changing just one letter in each of the words in the chains below, that's how!

(P.S. We've given you some clues in case you get stuck.)

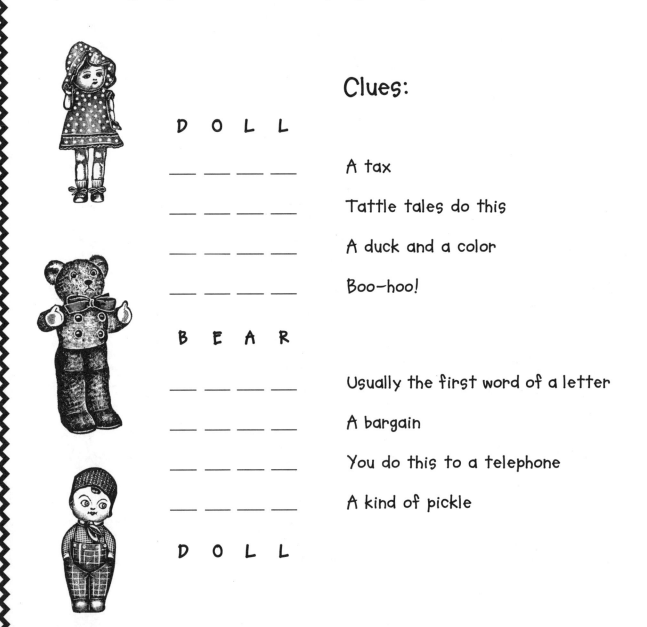

Clues:

D O L L

___ ___ ___ ___   A tax

___ ___ ___ ___   Tattle tales do this

___ ___ ___ ___   A duck and a color

___ ___ ___ ___   Boo—hoo!

B E A R

___ ___ ___ ___   Usually the first word of a letter

___ ___ ___ ___   A bargain

___ ___ ___ ___   You do this to a telephone

___ ___ ___ ___   A kind of pickle

D O L L

Do You Remember?

This is what a typical day at school for Dolly and Ted looks like. Study this scene for a few minutes, and when you're ready, turn the page to answer the questions about it. No fair—or fun—to sneak a peek!

Do You Remember?

Let's see how sharp your memory is!

What are your answers to the following questions?

1. What is the weather like outside? _____

2. What time is it? _____

3. There are two "visitors" just outside the window.
   Who are they? _____

4. Dolly is holding something in her right hand. What is it? _____

5. What subject is Dolly studying? _____

6. What is in the cup on Dolly's desk? _____

7. What is Ted wearing? _____

8. There's something under Dolly's desk! What is it? _____

9. Somebody's thrown an object across the room.
   What is it? _____

10. What is written in Dolly's book? _____

Bonus for brainiacs!

A. Describe the object in question #4. How is it decorated?

_____

B. How many petals are on the flower that Ted is holding?

_____

Riddle in the Middle

Can you find the seven uppercase letters in the bear below? Once you've found them, unscramble them to figure out the answer to the riddle.

Q. Why didn't the teddy bear want any dessert?

A. He was ___ ___ ___ ___ ___ ___ ___ !

American Girl Talk

Let's hear it for the red, white and blue!

When you complete each word in the puzzle below with the correct four-letter fragment, you'll find out about some of the popular American Girl dolls.

ARAW   ARNE   ATIV   EEDO   ERVA   EXIC

IRGI   LACK   LOTH   MOTH   NNES   ONEE   ORSE

RAID   RIDI   SCAP   TION   TRIB   VERY

Kaya is a N_____e American girl from the Nez Perce _____e. She has her own horse to ride and wears her long b_____ hair in b_____s.

Felicity Merriman is growing up in V_____nia, just before the start of the Revolu_____ary War in 1776. Like Kaya, she loves _____ng h_____s, too.

Josefina Montoya's story takes place in New M_____o in 1824, while **Kirsten Larson** is a pi_____r girl in Mi_____ota in 1854. She's just arrived in America from f_____ay Sweden.

After e_____ing from slavery in 1864, **Addy Walker** and her mother have le_____d the true meaning of fr_____m .

It's 1904, and **Samantha Parkington** lives with her rich grand_____er. Although she can have all the toys and c_____es she wants, she learns that not e_____ little girl is as lucky. Her friend **Nellie O'Malley** works as a s_____nt in the house next door.

Reading Between the Lines

The answers to the clues below are hidden within the words in the right-hand column. All you'll need to do is cross off three or more letters in each word—and the letters that are left will spell out the correct answer. Check out the example to see what we mean.

Example:

It's fun to play with   __toy__   H̶I̶STORY̶

Los Angeles is one   _____   FELICITY

Not nice   _____   MERRIMAN

Large body of water   _____   JOSEFINA

What a cow might say   _____   MONTOYA

A school subject   _____   SAMANTHA

Goes on wall with brush   _____   PARKINGTON

A fib   _____   NELLIE

Where to shop   _____   O'MALLEY

13

Wild Guess

How much do you know about the teddy bear's wild cousins? Use the clues below to help fill in this crossword puzzle.

Across

1. This bear from China is black and white—and cute all over!

2. How'd he get here? This popular Australian animal isn't a bear at all, but a marsupial.

3. Chicago's baseball team, or another name for baby bears.

4. This South East Asian bear has the same name as that big yellow star that rises every morning.

5. This bear's nickname rhymes with "Liz."

Down

1. The Spectacled Bear from South America looks like he's wearing these on his face.

2. Brrr! It's always cold where this bear lives.

3. Yum, yum! It's sticky and sweet and just what the Sloth Bear (and Pooh, too) likes to eat.

4. Probably the only place you'll see #1 Across.

Picture This

Step right up and welcome to our Bear Fair! To find out more about the teddies we've invited to attend the fair, you'll have to decode our picture puzzle below.

Ever [H + 🐦 – B] of a split-level house? Well, the Berenstain

[B + 🪑🪑🪑 – CH] live in a split-level 🌳 !

[Smo + 🗝️] the Bear first appeared in 1944, and he is still working hard

to [T + 🔔 – B] us how to prevent forest [F + ⚙️⚙️ – T]. He always

wears a brown 🤠 with his name on it.

Born in [🍐 + u], Paddington Bear traveled to [L + 1 + don] when

he was orphaned. He was adopted by the Brown family, and his favorite

[🦶 – T + D] is marmalade.

[Win +))] the Pooh's best friends are Tigger and [🐷 + let].

They play in the [99 + 1] Acre Wood every day.

Your Bear's Horoscope

Are you ready for some fun? This activity works best if you have a friend, or friends, to help you. Whenever you see a blank space in the story below, ask your friend to give you an example of the type of word that we're asking for, and then write your friend's answers in the corresponding spaces. Be sure nobody but you can see the page, or it won't be as funny. When you're done, you can read the story out loud—but try not to laugh too much!

P.S. You can do this one on your own, too, but it'll be funnier if you don't read the story until you've filled in all the blanks.

P.P.S. See our definitions below if you're not sure what a certain type of word is.

P.P.P.S.: If you don't know your bear's exact birthday, use the date he or she came to live with you.

HELPFUL HINTS

ADJECTIVE:
Word that describes something or someone (fuzzy, pink, smelly)

NOUN:
Person, place or thing (mouse, gas station, toy)

EXCLAMATION:
A funny sound or noise ("Burp!" "Wow!")

VERB:
An action word (fly, jump, blow). Past tense means it already happened (jumped, ran, shivered)

turn page for Horoscopes

SILLY STORIES

Aries (March 21–April 19)

Who's that shouting _____ and
(exclamation)

showing off how well he can _____?
(verb)

Your Aries teddy, that's who! He needs

lots of exercise, so sign him up for the

_____ team. Just make sure he
(sport)

wears a _____ when it's below
(article of clothing)

_____ degrees or he may _____.
(number)   (verb)

Cancer (June 21–July 22)

Home, _____, home is your Cancer
(adjective)

teddy's favorite place to be! She also loves

to _____ with you, so bring her along
(verb)

whenever you go to _____.
(geographical location)

And take note—if she's having a "bad fur"

day, let her _____ by herself and she'll
(verb)

be _____ in no time.
(adjective)

Taurus (April 20–May 20)

Your Taurus teddy is a real couch

_____, and she loves to eat! _____
(vegetable)   (food)

salad and _____ cookies are big
(another food)

taste treats for her. A _____ musician,
(adjective)

she sings like _____ and will love
(name of person)

you forever if you give

her _____.
(plural noun)

Leo (July 23–August 22)

Who's the _____ of your household?
(part of body)

Your charming Leo teddy! No _____
(adjective)

lion, he'd wrestle a _____ for you!
(animal)

In return for his _____ love, you're
(adjective)

expected to _____ his fur and buy
(verb)

him the latest _____!
(plural noun)

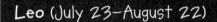

Gemini (May 21–June 20)

Variety is the _____ of life for your
(food)

Gemini teddy. He'll want to _____ in
(verb)

_____ one day and _____
(nearby place)   (verb)

in _____ the next! This brainy
(faraway place)

bear can also fix your _____ in
(noun)

_____ seconds flat.
(number)

Virgo (August 23–September 22)

Please don't leave any _____
(adjective)

_____ lying around your room—your
(plural noun)

Virgo teddy likes everything neat and

_____! Remember, he likes to
(adjective)

_____ at the same time every day, and
(verb)

keep his meals simple—a cup of hot

_____ and a _____ is perfect!
(beverage)   (food)

18

Libra (September 23–October 22)

Have a Libra teddy? Then you'll need at

least _____ more, because he hates to be
     (number)

alone. But if you _____ a party, he
                       (verb)

will decorate your _____ with
                    (place in your house)

beautiful _____ and serve the
              (plural noun)

finest _____ .
              (food)

Capricorn (December 22–January 19)

Your hard-working Capricorn teddy

needs a job—whether it's _____
                                (verb, ending in "ing")

the _____ or _____
         (noun)   (verb, ending in "ing")

the _____. And along with something
        (noun)

to do, give him at least _____ hugs a
                              (number)

day—not too tight, though, since he's got

sensitive _____ .
            (part of body, plural)

Scorpio (October 23–November 21)

Feeling _____ and _____ ?
          (adjective)   (adjective)

Your Scorpio teddy knows it! He's a bit

of a mystery to you, though, and may

disappear for _____ days and come back
                (number)

with a _____ . But if _____ ever
        (noun)   (name of person)

calls you a _____ _____ , he'll
             (adjective)   (animal)

be there to defend you.

Aquarius (January 20–February 18)

Some would call your Aquarian teddy

"weird," but we prefer _____ !
                          (adjective)

She's smart enough to learn how to

_____ a _____ , and she hates
  (verb)   (noun)

to be crowded. Make sure she always has

lots of room—a place to _____ as
                             (verb)

wide as a _____ , if you please!
            (large object)

Sagittarius (November 22–December 21)

Your Sag teddy is one happy bear—and

you can keep him feeling _____ by
                            (adjective)

making time for a game of _____ or
                               (sport)

capture the _____ . Some bears like
                (noun)

to get dressed up, but this guy would hate

_____ a _____ _____ .
(verb, ending in "ing") (adjective) (article of clothing)

He needs lots of room to _____ and _____ !
                           (verb)   (verb)

Pisces (February 19–March 20)

Pisces teds are affectionate and will

love to cuddle on your _____ .
                          (part of body)

They're also creative, so give yours

some jars of _____ , _____
                (liquid)   (adjective)

pencils and _____ and she'll make
              (plural noun)

_____ art!
 (adjective)

Find the Teddy Bear

Wanna play catch?

First you'll have to find your way to Teddy.

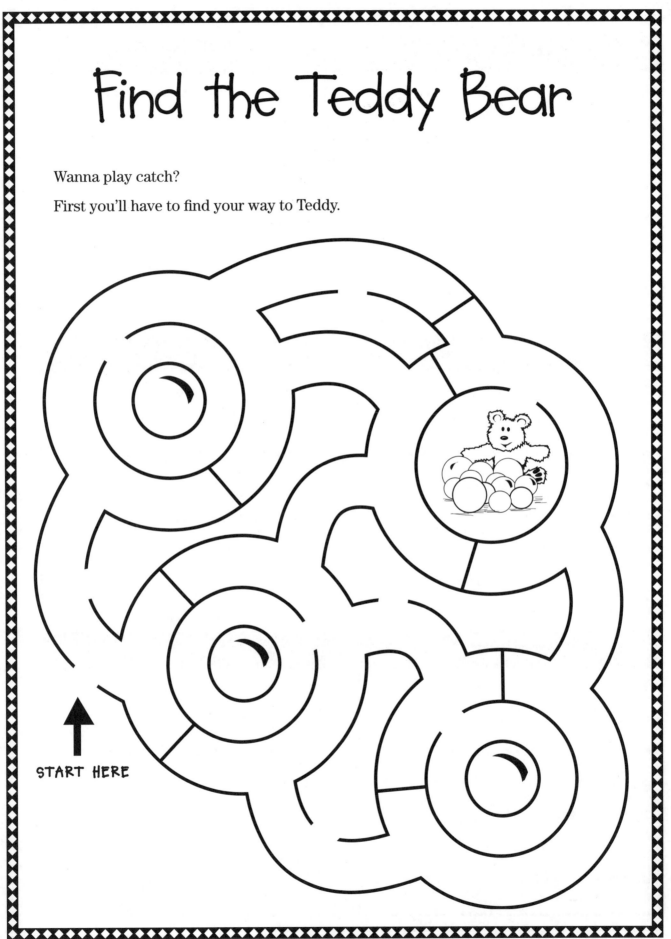

START HERE

20

Beary Special Spelling Bee

The capitalized words in the sentences below may sound the same, but they are spelled differently and mean different things. Put on your spelling caps and circle the words that are spelled correctly in each sentence.

A bear's claws are on his PAUSE. PAWS.

"Smell—o, world!" says Teddy. "My NOSE KNOWS tells me that dinner's ready!"

Name one great thing about teddies, please.
Unlike dogs, they don't get FLEAS. FLEES.

If Fuzzy Wuzzy was a BEAR, BARE, then Fuzzy Wuzzy had no HARE. HAIR.

What happens when a grizzly growls too much?
He gets HOARSE, HORSE, of course.

Where, oh where has Teddy's tail gone?
Do you think we need to SO SEW one on?

Did you get 'em all?
Good for EWE! YOU!

21

A Mix-up Fixed Up

Have you ever wondered what your teddies and dolls do when you're at school? Guess what? They don't sit around and wait for you to come home! Take the case of Amber, a little girl from New York City who has dolls and teddies from all over the world.

"I'll be back after class!" announced Amber as she headed for her bedroom door. Ten pairs of eyes stared back at her. They belonged to the ten wooden dolls that her grandmother had just brought back from a faraway trip.

"As if you guys could actually understand me!" laughed Amber, heading out . . .

. . . and leaving her dolls in a total, complete, utter state of panic!

Now, these ten little dolls were actually two sets of sisters. As you can see in the picture, the five apple-cheeked girls are, from oldest to youngest, Olga, Maria, Tatyana, Minka and Ivanka. And the teddy family, from teeniest to tallest, are Cassandra, Cornelia, Christina, Courtney and Colleen.

But that's *not* what you see in the picture at all! For in her rush to get to dance class, Amber had accidentally switched Cornelia and Minka when she was playing with them. This is usually not a problem when dolls are familiar with each other—but when they've just moved into a new home, it's a different story!

Olga　　**Maria**　　**Tatyana**　　**Cornelia**　　**Ivanka**

"A bear!!! She's going to eat us!" gasped Olga as she stared at Cornelia, very dramatically as if she were about to faint.

Cornelia, however, was far too terrified to be hungry. (Even if she were, she'd much prefer a yummy honeycomb!)

Meanwhile, Cornelia's sisters were positive that Minka was a fur trapper who wanted to cash in on the coats on their backs! "Bear hides are worth a lot of money—especially fur as plush and luxurious as ours," Colleen sputtered, shivering at the thought.

As you can guess, Minka wasn't a fur trapper. And when the sisters realized there was nothing to be frightened of, they grew rather, well, haughty. "We hail from a very noble family," boasted Tatyana. "Dolls like us were first made in the 1890s, by skilled artisans living in thick forests in Russia."

"No wonder you look so old and decrepit!" shot back Christina. "Teddy bears were first created in the early 1900s!"

"Big deal!" answered Maria. "Dolls like us were taken into space by Russian astronauts!"

"That's nothing!" yelled Courtney. "We heard that A-Rod, the New York Yankees all-star third baseman, keeps a teddy bear on the dashboard of his car!"

"Don't mess with us!" threatened Tatyana. "We may only have five in our family, but the biggest doll like us contained 72 pieces!"

Cassandra   Minka   Christina   Courtney   Colleen

At the thought of 72 of these screaming creatures, Cornelia burst into tears. She couldn't even *count* to 72! Hearing the little bear sob, the sisters realized that perhaps they had gone too far.

"Now we've done it," Olga looked at her sisters. "We need to put our heads together and decide what to do."

And when she said they should put their heads together, she meant it—literally! Olga unscrewed Maria's head, while Maria unscrewed Tatyana's head, and Tatyana said, "Since Minka's not here, Ivanka will have to stack up inside me. It won't be a perfect fit, but . . ."

"I'm just about the right size!" piped up Cornelia, who had been watching all along. And she began to unscrew her own head!

"How can you, a mere bear, possibly know our secret?" asked Ivanka.

Answered Cornelia, "We're nesting dolls, too! Just look!" And she pointed across the room at Colleen, Courtney, Christina and Cassandra, who were in various stages of the very same unscrewing procedure. The bear sisters turned around all at once when they heard Cornelia.

"I must see this for myself!" cried Olga, who headed over to the teddies. Maria, Tatyana and Ivanka were right behind her.

"They're just like us!" exclaimed Courtney when she saw the dolls.

. . . and soon everyone was chatting and laughing and swiveling and unswiveling, and the party continued on and on until . . .

Uh oh! Amber's back! Like a flash, the dolls lined up just as you see in the picture.

"Hey, guys," greeted Amber. "Did you miss me when I was gone?"

Mamma Mia!

The nesting dolls you just read about are called *Matryoshka*. That term comes from the word *mater*, which is Russian for "mother." There are moms everywhere, of course, but they aren't called "mom" everywhere! See if you can figure out what she's called in other countries by playing the matching game below.

1. Mum   A. Spain

2. Maman   B. France

3. Mom   C. England

4. Mutter   D. United States

5. Madre   E. Germany

I Want My Mommy—or Daddy!

Teddies may not look exactly like their human buddies, but sometimes friends act and dress alike. Look at the teddies and the children below. Can you match up the teddies with their owners? (Hint: They may be wearing—or doing—something the same.) Draw a line from the bear to their Mommy—or Daddy.

Doll House Dilemma

Three girls live right next to each other in Dollywood, California, and each girl has a number-one favorite doll. Using the clues below to fill in the answer box, can you figure out where each girl lives and the name of her favorite doll?

Clues:

1. Talisha lives in the middle house.

2. April doesn't have a Swan Lake Barbie.

3. Raggedy Ann is Nicky's favorite doll.

4. One of the dolls is Polly Pocket.

5. Nicky doesn't live in the last house.

Girl's Name			
Favorite Doll			

Simply "D" Lightful

Study the picture at right carefully.

How many objects can you find in the scene that begin with the letter "D"?

Write your answers on the lines below.

_____   _____

_____   _____

_____   _____

_____   _____

_____   _____

_____   _____

_____   _____

_____   _____

That's the Spirit!

The Native American Hopi people make some very special dolls called *kachinas*. Learn more about them by reading "Hello, Dolly" on pages 33–36 and by completing this puzzle. When you're done, the letters in the bold boxes will spell out the meaning of the word "Hopi."

1. A kachina doll is made to represent this. It can be good or, not too often, evil!

2. The Hopis are a Native _____ people.

3. Phoenix is the capital of the state where the Hopi nation is based.

4. The special outfit worn by a kachina; also, what an actor wears in a play.

5. The Hopis believe kachina spirits can help bring a good one of these in the fall.

6. Forget plain old black and white! Kachina dolls can be described as this.

7. Since all kachinas are made by hand, no two are alike. What's another word for one-of-a-kind?

8. Hopi children believe in kachinas just like other kids believe in Santa _____.

Did You Miss Me?

Barbie has had many friends and relatives over the years! Which one of her doll pals is *not* hidden in the puzzle?

MIDGE   KEN   TERESA   TUTTI

SKIPPER   STACIE   KELLY   KRISSY

```
R   E   P   P   I   K   S   N
A   K   R   I   S   S   E   B
T   E   R   E   S   K   C   D
E   G   D   I   M   F   Y   A
I   U   H   Q   S   L   G   S
C   X   O   J   L   S   O   E
A   P   W   E   L   V   Y   R
T   R   K   D   Y   N   A   T
S   E   G   I   T   T   U   T
```

Hello, Dolly!

Did you ever wonder what the first doll in the world looked like? You'll probably never know—and, in fact, nobody even knows exactly when the first doll was made—or who made it. But we do know that children have played with human-like figures, even if they were just made from sticks or clay, since the beginning of time.

People have always made objects shaped like themselves. The earliest ones we recognize as dolls were made in about 2000 B.C. in Egypt. Usually they were just wood cut into a paddle shape—so we call them paddle dolls, but who knows what an Egyptian child called them? Sometimes they were simple jointed figures stuffed with linen or papyrus leaves. We know girls in ancient times loved their dolls as much as girls today do; the remnants of Mt. Vesuvius, a volcano that destroyed two cities in 79 A.D., include a girl holding a doll tightly in her hands, trying to protect it from the lava and ashes.

German wooden Grödner Tal couple, circa 1820s

Dolls haven't always been just playthings. Because they look like people, they have often been used for magical and religious rituals. When a girl in ancient Greece got married (at the ripe old age of 12 or 13!) she went to the temple with her dolls and dedicated them to one of the goddesses—Hera, protector of marriage, or Aphrodite, goddess of love, or Artemis, protector of women and children—in a special ceremony that showed she was leaving childhood behind. And the Native American Hopi people, who believe the Kachina spirits help bring rain and a good harvest, have always made brightly colored Kachina dolls to represent these spirits.

For centuries, dolls for play were usually made at home from materials that a girl, or her mother or father, had at hand: wood, cloth, leather, dried apples or corn husks. By the 1300s

German felt dolls by Steiff, circa 1910–1917

American cloth doll by Izannah Walker, circa 1870s

English wooden Queen Anne, circa 1700s

French porcelain bébé by A. Thuillier, circa 1880s

French porcelain bébé by Schmitt & Fils, circa 1880s

wealthy families were able to buy dolls for their children. Today a girl's first doll might be a baby doll, but until about 300 years ago all dolls were made to look like adults. Just as children were dressed as miniature adults until the mid-1700s, so were dolls. Strangely enough, they weren't called dolls then—they were called babies!

Those first dolls that girls could buy were made of wood, with jointed arms and legs, painted faces and fancy clothing. Some of the earliest of these that survive were made in England in the 1700s, and are called Queen Annes—not because they looked anything like a queen, but because Queen Anne was alive and ruling in England then. At first these dolls were beautifully carved by hand with great care. By about 1750, they started to be produced in large numbers and with much less care, because the English were trying to compete with dollmakers from a part of Germany known as the Grödner Tal. The cheaper wooden dolls became known as "penny woodens," (can you guess why?) or "Dutch dolls"—not because they came from Holland but because the German word for German is *deutsch*, which sounds a lot like Dutch!

Soon other materials began to be used for making dolls: papier-mâché, china and wax were the most popular. Most dolls were made in Germany and England, but by the 1800s, Americans made dolls, too. One of the more famous early American dollmakers is a woman named Izannah Walker, from Rhode Island, who made and sold sturdy oil-painted cloth dolls in the second half of the 1800s.

The French had not been very active in dollmaking, but around 1860 the most gorgeous dolls ever seen, produced in that country, began appearing on the shelves of fancy toy shops in Europe, with names like *Au Paradis des Enfants* (In a Children's Paradise). Made of fragile porcelain, with mohair wigs, glass eyes and sumptuous wardrobes, these were for wealthy children only. Some lucky American girls received them as gifts from rich relatives traveling abroad. When we look at these dolls, wearing silks and velvets, earrings and tiny leather shoes, we understand why the years of 1860–1900 are sometimes called The Golden Age of Dollmaking.

Some of the names used for dolls come from strange, often sad, stories. For example, stiff porcelain dolls made in one piece in the 1800s were known as Frozen Charlottes, after the story of a little girl who froze to death on an icy night.

English porcelain Frozen Charlottes, circa 1800s

Whether or not poor Charlotte ever existed, one of everybody's favorite dolls came into being because of a true sad story. In 1915 an American political cartoonist named Johnny Gruelle, whose young daughter Marcella was seriously ill, found an old rag doll in the attic, named it Raggedy Ann, and gave it to Marcella. She loved the doll and the stories her father made up about her. A year later Marcella died, but the stories lived on in the books that Johnny published. The Gruelle family began making dolls of Raggedy Ann to go with the books. Today Raggedy Ann and her friend Raggedy Andy are still made and still loved by children.

American cloth Raggedy Anns and Andys by Georgene Novelties, circa 1930s

Some of the most popular dolls of the 20th century have been those that look like celebrities. One of the first companies to make a celebrity doll was an American company named Ideal, which convinced the most popular child star of the 1930s, curly-haired Shirley Temple, to let them turn her into a doll. It took 28 attempts to get the likeness right. One of Ideal's competitors, Madame Alexander, an American woman who had started the Alexander Doll Company in 1923, told everybody she thought it was a bad idea to exploit a child by making a doll of it—but then quickly began to make dolls of some of the most famous children of the 1930s, like the Canadian Dionne Quintuplets (five babies born at the same time to the same mother!) and the American movie star Margaret

American composition Shirley Temples by Ideal, circa 1930s

O'Brien. Madame Alexander also made dolls from favorite books and movies, such as Little Women, Cinderella and Sleeping Beauty. Madame Alexander is no longer alive, but her company, more than 80 years old and still located in New York City, continues to make dolls of famous people, movies and books, among others.

Hard plastic Cherry Twins by Madame Alexander, circa 1957

Italian cloth girl by Lenci, circa 1930s

Probably the most famous doll of the 20th century was Barbie. She was introduced in 1959 by Mattel, a company that still makes her today. Barbie was the idea of Ruth Handler, who owned Mattel together with her husband, Elliot. Ruth used to watch her ten-year-old daughter, Barbara, playing with her grown-up paper dolls and she decided that girls should have real dolls that looked like teenagers and had wonderful wardrobes, just like paper dolls. She could see that girls didn't only want to play at being mothers and take care of baby dolls; they wanted to play at being older girls. She had a hard time convincing the toy stores that anybody would buy such a doll, but the girls of America quickly proved Ruth right! By the way, Ruth also had a son; can you guess what his name was? (It has three letters and begins with "K.")

American vinyl Barbie doll by Mattel, circa 1960s

American vinyl Barbie dolls by Mattel, circa 1960s

Barbie, along with the Cabbage Patch Kids, the American Girl dolls and Bratz, is still among children's favorite toys. These popular dolls, like the earlier ones you've read about, make up just a small part of the history of these playthings. You can see that although dolls have changed a lot since ancient times, children's love for them seems timeless.

Katie

Ginnie Hofmann

Can You Imagine a World Without Teddy Bears?

Once upon a time, and not that long ago, either, there were no teddy bears. This may be hard to believe as you snuggle under the covers with your favorite teddy, but children growing up more than 100 years ago did not have teddies to cuddle with. Girls had dolls, of course, and there were stuffed animals to play with, but these were often made of scratchy wool and filled with hard wood shavings (a stuffing called excelsior) so they weren't cozy enough for cuddling.

German mohair teddy bear by Steiff, circa 1920s

In the 19th century, some of the best stuffed animals were being made in Germany. Margarete Steiff, an expert seamstress who had been crippled with polio as a child, had started making felt and velvet animals in 1880. Her animals became very popular in many countries, including America. They became so popular that Margarete soon had to hire other people to help make her toys. Before long, she was running a busy, successful toy factory from her wheelchair.

Margarete's brother, Fritz, helped her run the business side of her company. Fritz had a large family of six boys and three girls. His second son, Richard, loved drawing, and was very good at it. Both his father and his aunt encouraged his talents, sending him to art school in the city of Stuttgart when he grew older. Richard had always loved bears, and he spent a lot of his time in Stuttgart sketching bears he saw in zoos and circuses. In letters to his family, Richard wrote about

American mohair teddy bear by Ideal, circa 1906

German mohair bears by Steiff, circa 1906–1957

41

his love for bears, and about his idea of someday making a cuddly toy for boys. He knew that people said boys should not play with dolls, but he also knew that boys, just like girls, sometimes need a soft toy to hug. During his years in Stuttgart, Richard began to think about making a stuffed bear boys would not be embarrassed to cuddle.

It would be several years before Richard could concentrate on his idea. When he was 20, he went to work for his Aunt Margarete's toy company, selling the popular elephants, dogs, monkeys and rabbits to stores all around the world and making up designs for new animals, many of them based on his sketches from the Stuttgart zoo. The animals Richard designed were especially lifelike, compared to the toy animals other companies made, because he had observed the real animals in the zoo. When his

older brother Paul, who was an excellent designer, also began working for Aunt Margarete's company, the brothers came up with even more clever ways to make Richard's designs into three-dimensional stuffed animals. They used movable joints to attach the heads and limbs, and were very careful how they stuffed the animals. Stuffing, after all, was what gave them their true shapes. Among the many animals the Steiff company made in the last years

German mohair teddy bears by Steiff, circa 1904–05

of the 19th century were elephants, tigers, lions, monkeys, camels—and lots of bears. There were pull-along bears on all fours on metal wheels, standing bears on wooden roly-poly bases, bears with growlers inside and dancing bears. Wealthy parents all over the world bought these toys for their children.

But Richard, busy as he was designing animals and traveling around the world to sell them, had not forgotten his idea of a cuddly bear for boys. In 1902 he finally tried his hand at it, and created a 21½-inch-high dark-colored bear with a hump at the back of its neck. It was very true-to-life, but when Aunt Margarete saw it, she thought it was too big, too heavy and too expensive for children to play with. In

American mohair teddy bear by Hecla, circa 1907

February 1903, Richard took his bear to America with the other new toys for the year, and found Aunt Margarete was right. Nobody liked his bear much.

Richard returned to Germany and went back to work. By the end of 1903, he had made a smaller, lighter jointed mohair bear with long arms and legs, a smaller hump and a nose made of sealing wax. He was light-colored mohair, and Richard called him, simply, *Bär*, the German word for bear. He didn't look as much like a real bear, but he was plump and soft and much more appealing.

This time, Richard's younger brother, Franz, who was now working alongside Richard and Paul at Aunt Margarete's toy company, took *Bär* to the World's Fair in St. Louis in 1904, to introduce him to America. Everyone fell in love with this cuddly creation and wanted to buy him. *Bär* won a gold medal and the best prize of all, the Grand Prix of the World's Fair.

American wool plush teddy bear, possibly by Miller Manufacturing, circa 1908

Now that they had the perfect cuddly bear, the Steiffs wanted to be sure nobody could copy it. Franz came up with the idea of putting a tiny metal button in the left ear of their bears—and all their other animals, too—so everybody would know the bear was made by Steiff. (To this day, every stuffed animal made at the Steiff factory in Germany has a metal button in its left ear.)

Why was Richard Steiff's little *Bär* so popular in the United States? Certainly, he was cute, but there was probably another important reason—and it has to do with why he became called a teddy.

American mohair teddy bear, possibly by Bruin, circa 1907

During the years that Richard Steiff was trying to create the perfect cuddly bear toy, the president of the United States was Theodore Roosevelt, known to everyone as Teddy. Teddy Rooosevelt loved hunting, and he especially loved bear hunting. In November 1902 he took a four-day hunting trip in Mississippi, but had no luck. Not a single bear could be found for his hunting pleasure. The people who had invited him on the trip were embarrassed and upset that the President was not having a good time, so they finally captured a bear cub and tied it to a tree so the President could shoot at it. President Roosevelt, naturally, refused to kill such a young bear—a helpless baby who had no chance of escaping!

The American people loved President Roosevelt, and this story made him even more popular. The cartoonist Clifford Berryman drew a cartoon in the

November 18, 1902, *Washington Post* newspaper entitled "Drawing the Line in Mississippi," showing President Roosevelt refusing to kill the cub. The bear soon became President Roosevelt's mascot.

While Richard Steiff probably didn't see or hear the story about President Roosevelt and the cub, an American candy-store owner, Morris Michtom, did. His son, Benjamin, says that his parents saw the cartoon and decided to make a toy bear cub. His mother, Rose, sewed up a few samples and sent one to President Roosevelt, asking if it would be all right to call the bear "Teddy's Bear" in memory

German mohair teddy bear by Steiff, circa 1920s

of the Mississippi hunting trip. Benjamin reports that the President wrote back saying he did not think his name was worth much to the toy-bear business, but that the Michtoms were welcome to use it. So Morris and Rose started making and selling *their* stuffed toy bear in 1903. By 1904—the same year Franz Steiff brought *Bär* from Germany to the St. Louis World's Fair—they had so many orders that they had to open a factory to make teddy bears. They named their company the Ideal Novelty and Toy Company and went on to make many other popular toys throughout the 20th century. Pretty soon the bears Steiff

German mohair teddy bear by Steiff, circa 1904

was making and selling in the United States and all over the world were also known as Teddy's Bears. And it wasn't long before lots of companies in America, Germany and other countries, were all making and selling teddy bears.

You can see that Rose and Morris Michtom were making their bears at exactly the same time Richard Steiff was making his. Who do you think made the first Teddy Bear?

Tuxedo Teddy

Bandanna Bear

Connect the Dots

Connect the dots and color him in!

A Rare Bear

Steiff has been making teddies for more than 100 years—and collectors are always on the lookout for the oldest and rarest bears. Steiff made some very special bears in 1912, in memory of the many people who died when a ship sank off the coast of England. You can find out more about the bear by using the clues to complete the puzzle below. You may need to refer to the story on pages 41–44 for some of the answers. (When you are done, the letters in the bold boxes will spell out the name of this famous ship.)

Clues:

1. Like all Steiff animals, this teddy has a button in his ear. Which ear?

2. The ship sunk on the 14th of this month—the 4th month in the year.

3. This special teddy is 50 cm tall. What does cm stand for?

4. Most old teddies are brown or honey-colored. But this guy's the _____ sheep of the family!

5. 600 of these special bears were sent to this city in England.

6. Kind of wool used to make Steiff teddies.

7. One of these special teddies was sold for thousands of dollars to the highest bidder at an _____

D_lls Fr_m J_p_n!

Hey, where have all the vowels gone? We need A, E, I, O and yoU to complete this puzzle. Use the clues to help you fill in the missing vowels in the words below while you learn about Hina Matsuri—an annual holiday in Japan when people display special dolls.

(P.S. The letters in the circles will spell out two words that describe YOU!)

___ ___ ___ ___ ___ ___ ___ ___ ___ ___ ___ ___ ___ ___

G _ R L '(S) D _ Y — Until recently, this was celebrated on the same day as Hina Matsuri (Hint: Not boy's, but...)

(M)(O)(R) C H — Hina Matsuri falls on the third day of this month.

_ L (T) _ R — Japanese families display their dolls on one of these. (Hint: Spelled differently, it's what you do to clothes that don't fit.)

P _ _(C)H — Flower power! Blossoms from this fruit tree are traditional holiday decorations.

_ M P _ R(O)R — Many Hina Matsuri dolls are dressed like this long-ago ruler of Japan. (Hint: There's a famous folk tale about one and his "new clothes.")

T(O)(K)Y _ — Japan's capital city

F _ S T(O)V _ L — Time to party!

(O)M P R _ S S — Wife of long-ago ruler of Japan

51

Reading Between the Lines

Now that you know the history of the teddy bear, here's your chance to really get the *inside* scoop! The answers to the clues at left are hidden within the words in the right-hand column. All you'll need to do is cross off one or more letters in each word—and the letters that are left will spell out the correct answer. Check out the example to see what we mean.

Example:

Not different _____ same _____ S̶EAMS̶TRES̶S̶

Not here _____ THEODORE

Chickens do it _____ ROOSEVELT

It's sweet! _____ STUTTGART

Not black or white _____ GERMANY

You'll find one onstage _____ FACTORY

Bees do it _____ STUFFING

Someone may send one on your birthday _____ RICHARD

Doesn't bend _____ STE̶IFF

You do this with a straw _____ MISSISSIPPI

Close this to get some shut-eye _____ CLIFFORD

String, jelly, or pinto _____ BERRYMAN

Changing Faces

Many of the dolls that you play with are made from vinyl and plastic, but these materials weren't around centuries ago. Dollmakers used whatever they could find—everything from clay and corn husks to apples and wood!

How can we keep up with the "changing face" of the doll? It's easy to go from CLAY to WOOD by replacing just one letter in each of the words in the chain below.

Clues:

C L A Y

____ ____ ____ ____   What you do after a concert or play

____ ____ ____ ____   One fine fellow

____ ____ ____ ____   You can do this to vegetables or wood

____ ____ ____ ____   Where chickens are

____ ____ ____ ____   He's got a mask and a ringed tail

C O R N

____ ____ ____ ____   What's left when you eat an apple

____ ____ ____ ____   A real dud

____ ____ ____ ____   Past tense of wear

____ ____ ____ ____   You just wrote one

W O O D

The Day My Teddy Bear Came To School With Me

This activity works best if you have a friend, or friends, to help you. Whenever you see a blank space in the story below, ask your friend to give you an example of the type of word that we're asking for, and then write your friend's answers in the corresponding spaces. Be sure nobody but you can see the page, or it won't be as funny. When you're done, you can read the story out loud—but try not to laugh too much!

P.S. You can do this one on your own, too, but it'll be funnier if you don't read the story until you've filled in all the blanks.

P.P.S. See our definitions at right if you're not sure what a certain type of word is.

One morning I was eating my usual breakfast of _____ _____,
(number)   (type of food, plural)

when my teddy bear _____ in to the room carrying a _____ .
(verb, past tense)   (noun)

"I'm ready for school!" he said. "Let's go!"

Our first class of the day was gym with _____ . We warmed up
(name of teacher in school)

by doing _____ sit-ups and _____ push-ups and stretching our _____ .
(number)   (number)   (part of the body, plural)

Then, we _____ around the _____ for _____ .
(verb, past tense)   (room in school)   (length of time)

After a _____ game of _____ , we were all
(adjective)   (name of sport or game)

_____ with sweat! The best part is, my teddy bear _____
(verb, ending in "ing")   (verb, past tense)

_____ points, and his team won with a score of _____ to _____ !
(number)   (high number)   (low number)

Next, we had band practice. My teddy

bear picked up a _____ and started to
              (musical instrument)

_____ . It sounded _____!
(verb, present tense)   (adjective)

It was incredible how well he played _____
                                 (name of song)

—even better than _____!
               (name of classmate)

Up next was a _____ test in
             (adjective)

_____ class. But when my teddy bear
(name of subject in school)

read the first question on the exam—"Name the

first _____ of _____ —he decided he
   (occupation)   (name of country)

was feeling _____ and wanted to go to _____ .
        (adjective)   (place)

"School is _____ , but I would not want to _____ there every
      (adjective)   (verb)

day!" he told me.

"I can't wait to relax, have some _____ and watch _____!"
                              (food)   (name of television show)

HELPFUL HINTS

ADJECTIVE: Word that describes something or someone (fuzzy, pink, smelly)

NOUN: Person, place or thing (mouse, gas station, toy)

EXCLAMATION: A funny sound or noise ("Burp!" "Wow!")

VERB: An action word (fly, jump, blow). Past tense means it already happened (jumped, ran, shivered)

A Little Bit "Mo"

You met Morris "Mo" Michtom, teddy bear maker extraordinaire, in our history of the teddy bear on pages 41–44. He and his company, the Ideal Novelty and Toy Company, made other popular toys for tots, too. To find out a little bit "mo," finish each word in the puzzle below with the correct four-letter fragment from this list.

```
ROOF    RITN    TTLE
ROKE    COLO    RYTH
AKAB    RAGI    NOVA    OOKE
ETSY    MOUS    TTEM
CCEE    ELAI    ESSE    EARS
```

Morris "Mo" Michtom loved eve_____ing about teddy bears—but there was one thing he didn't like about dolls. Made of f_____le porc_____n, they were easily b_____n.

What good was a doll you couldn't play with? So Mo made sure that every toy that Ideal made was unbre_____le.

Mo had other in_____tive ideas, too. He invented a doll called B_____ Wetsy. Guess what she did after she drank out of her bo_____?!

Ideal also made dolls based on the Campbell Soup kids. They were dr_____d in bright red and white, just like the _____rs on the soup can.

In 1934, Ideal made a doll that l_____d like Shirley Temple, a child star more fa_____ in her day than B_____ey Sp_____ is today! It took 28 a_____pts to get the doll exactly right. Now there's p_____ that if at first you don't su_____d, try, try again!

Picture This

If you're reading this, there's a good chance you have—or know someone who has—a Barbie doll. Can you believe that the very first Barbie doll was made in 1959? We've got tons more fun facts to share. You'll just have to decode our picture puzzle to find out more!

[Bar + 🐝] has had more than [8 + T] [🚗 + eers] —everything from a [rock + ⭐] to a doctor!

The best-selling [Bar + 🐝] ever was [✋ + tal + E] Hair [Bar + 🐝]. She had hair from her 👧 to her 🦶.

[Bar + 🐝]'s 5 sisters R Skipper, [2 + T], [Sta + C], [(k + 🔔 − B) + E] and Krissy.

[Bar + 🐝] has had a [chim + 🍳 + Z], a [🍳 + da], and a lion [(☕ − P) + B] as pets.

Star Quality

You may love Barbies and Bratz, but did you ever wonder what girls played with a long time ago? Use the clues to fill out the crossword grid, and when you're done, you'll find out the name of a popular doll based on a famous actress from the 1930s. We've even filled in one of the boxes to get you started!

1. This doll is named after a famous movie _____. (Hint: Twinkle, twinkle)

2. She was known for her curly _____.

3. Her movies featured lots of _____ and dancing.

4. In the 1930s, movies were often called motion _____.

5. This actress is well known for performing a song called "On the Good Ship _____." (Hint: It's the name of a candy on a stick that you lick.)

6. Hers were hazel.

7. She specialized in this kind of dance. (Hint: Shuffle step, shuffle ball change)

8. One of her most popular films was called "Stand Up and _____." (Hint: Think football games and pom-poms.)

9. She had a great big one of these. (Hint: Say cheese!)

10. A small hollow in a person's cheek that looks cute when he or she grins. (She was famous for hers!)

11. More than 6 _____ dolls that looked like her were sold. (Hint: 6,000,000)

12. She got her start in the movies at this age. (Hint: One, two, _____)

Snack Attack

Crunchie, Munchie and Scrunchie are triplets. And like most teddies, they love sweet treats. But Mama Bear's one smart cookie! She makes her sons work for their fun! By studying the clues below to fill out the answer box, can you figure out each teddy's favorite snack—and the chore he must complete in order to get some?

Clues:

1. Munchie is allergic to strawberry Jello, but doesn't mind taking out the garbage.

2. Gummy worms are one of the bears' favorite treats.

3. One of the chores is washing the dishes.

4. Crunchie loves chocolate chip cookies.

5. Scrunchie never mows the lawn.

	Crunchie	Munchie	Scrunchie
Favorite Treat			
Chore			

History Mystery

We've found a letter that an American girl named Rebecca wrote to her Aunt Sophie. It's dated 1885, but it appears that Rebecca was very clever and decided to write in a secret code! We think we've cracked the code, but we need your help to figure out exactly what the letter says. (Hint: Rebecca's "bébé" was made during what is known as "The Golden Age of Dollmaking.")

May 10, 1885

Dear Aunt Sophie,

20.8.1.14.11   25.15.21   6.15.18   13.25   "2.5.2.5,"   1.19

25.15.21   19.1.25   9.14   6.18.1.14.3.5.

8.5.18   3.21.18.12.19   1.18.5   12.9.11.5   7.15.12.4.5.14

19.21.14.19.8.9.14.5,   1.14.4   8.5.18   2.18.15.23.14

5.25.5.19   19.16.1.18.11.12.5!

9   1.13   19.15   12.21.3.11.25   20.15   8.1.22.5

8.5.18,   1.14.4   9   1.13   22.5.18.25   3.1.18.5.6.21.12

23.8.5.14   9   8.15.12.4   8.5.18.

9   8.15.16.5   20.15   19.1.9.12   20.15   5.21.18.15.16.5

15.14.5   4.1.25,   2.21.20   21.14.20.9.12   20.8.5.14,

1.21   18.5.22.15.9.18!

Love,
Rebecca

SECRET CODE:
A=1 B=2 C=3 D=4 E=5 F=6 G=7 H=8 I=9 J=10 K=11 L=12 M=13 N=14
O=15 P=16 Q=17 R=18 S=19 T=20 U=21 V=22 W=23 X=24 Y=25 Z=26

Let's Have a PINKnic!

Ever had a tea party with your dolls and teddies? Why not jazz things up a bit and have a *pink*nic?! The recipes below are yummy and easy to make, but just be sure to let an adult know that you will be taking over the kitchen!

Can you guess what color the guests have to wear?

FRUITY PATOOTIE

Ingredients
1 teaspoon unsweetened powdered drink mix, such as Kool-Aid
  (any flavor you like, as long as it's pink!)
½ cup instant powdered milk
3½ tablespoons sugar
3 cups cold water

Directions
Mix the first 3 ingredients together in a large plastic bottle.
  (You can use an empty soda bottle that you have rinsed out.)

Next, add the cold water and put the cap back on. Make sure it's
  tightly closed, and shake the bottle until the liquid gets fluffy and
  frothy on top.

Drink right away before the fluff goes away!

Makes 2 servings

STRAWBERRY SHORTSANDWICH

You'll need to make the filling for this recipe at least 3 hours before your PINKnic.

Ingredients
Thin white bread, crusts removed

Filling
4 tablespoons butter or margarine, room temperature
1 cup confectioners (powdered) sugar
1 tablespoon lemon juice
7 to 10 large strawberries

Directions
Using a hand mixer, blend butter until it's creamy. (You can also use a blender or electric mixer, but you'll need to ask an adult to plug it in and use it with you.) Add sugar and lemon juice and blend well.

Next, mix in the strawberries until everything is thick and creamy. (You may have to add more strawberries or sugar until the filling looks like it will be easy to spread.)

When you are done with that, transfer the mixture to the refrigerator and let it chill for about 3 hours.

When it's chilled, spread on your bread (thin slices work the best) and cut into triangles or use a cookie cutter to make fun shapes. If you want to, you can put some peanut butter on your strawberry shortsandwiches, too!

PINK PANDA-MONIUM

Start this recipe at least 4½ hours before your PINKnic. You can also make it the day before.

Ingredients
1 cup whipping cream
¼ cup confectioners (powdered) sugar
½ teaspoon vanilla extract
A few drops of red food coloring
8½-ounce package of chocolate wafer cookies

Directions
Using a hand mixer, whip the cream together with the sugar, vanilla extract and food coloring until it is thick and fluffy—and pink! (You can also use a blender or electric mixer, but you'll need to ask an adult to plug it in and use it with you.)

Keep in mind that you may have to experiment with the amount of food coloring to get the right color, so start out with just a few drops. Set 1 cup of whipped cream aside.

Spread whipped cream on top of each cookie, and stack them up in groups of 5 on a plate lined with wax paper. Set in refrigerator to chill for 15 minutes.

Next, arrange the stacks in a log, setting them on their sides, on a large serving plate or loaf pan. Gently press them together and spread the leftover whipped cream on the top and sides. Cover with wax paper and put back in the fridge to chill for at least 4 hours.

When you're ready to serve, be sure to cut your Pink Panda-monium on a diagonal so you can really see the stripes.

Chef's tip: You can substitute a container of strawberry or plain Cool Whip for the whipping cream, sugar and vanilla extract.

If you want to get really fancy, you may decorate the top with pink M&Ms, or crush up a candy cane and sprinkle it on your PINK PANDA-MONIUM!

Serves 4 to 6 (or 1 very hungry teddy).

Did You Miss Me?

Which famous bear from the list below *cannot* be found hidden in the puzzle?

POOH
PADDINGTON
SMOKEY
SNUGGLE
YOGI
RUPERT
POOKY
CORDUROY

```
S  S  O  A  N  H  B  K
N  M  R  X  O  S  F  Y
U  O  U  O  T  N  U  O
G  K  D  B  G  U  T  R
G  E  R  J  N  G  H  U
L  Y  O  G  I  G  O  D
A  H  C  I  D  L  P  R
Y  C  O  L  D  E  Q  O
M  E  V  O  A  N  G  C
Z  T  R  E  P  U  R  W
```

Riddle in the Middle

You'll find all but seven letters of the alphabet in the doll's dress below. Once you've figured out which letters are missing, unscramble them to spell the name of one of the American Girl dolls.

(Hint: She's from Sweden.)

___ ___ ___ ___ ___ ___ ___

Pick a Number!

You've heard of a crossword puzzle? Well, this is more like a cross*number* puzzle! To find out the answer to the riddle, you'll first need to figure out the answers to the clues. Next, find the letter listed above #1 in the clues below and write that letter in box #1—and continue until you've filled in all 22 boxes.

What is black and white and black and white and black and white?

Clues:

Not in the sea, but on _____.

‾10 ‾18 ‾4 ‾5

Where you rest your head in bed.

‾2 ‾20 ‾21 ‾22 ‾8 ‾16

Hello in Hawaii.

‾3 ‾9 ‾15 ‾19 ‾1

Another word for smile.

‾13 ‾7 ‾11 ‾17

What "&" stands for.

‾6 ‾12 ‾14

Bearigami

You've heard of Origami, the Japanese art of paper folding? Well, we're gonna do *Bearigami*! All you'll need is a square piece of paper, 7 inches or larger, to make one very special teddy. You may need to ask an adult for help with some of the instructions, but we know you can do it!

There are two basic ways to fold paper in Origami, and you will use both to make your bear. As you can see in the picture, the Valley fold is an upward fold. When you see dashed lines, it means you should make a Valley fold. When you see dotted and dashed lines, you will make a Mountain, or downward, fold.

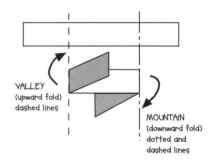

VALLEY
(upward fold)
dashed lines

MOUNTAIN
(downward fold)
dotted and
dashed lines

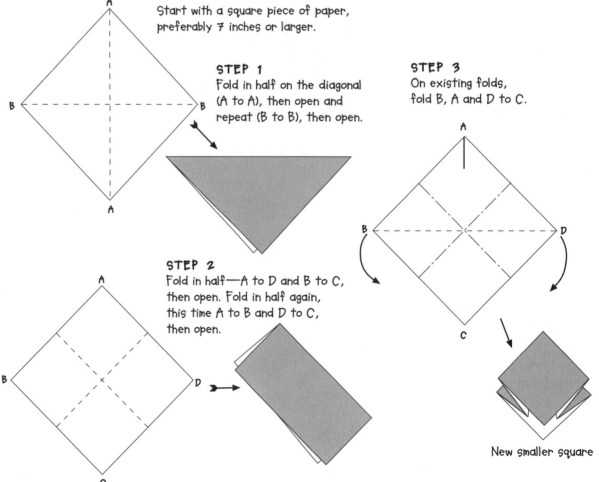

Start with a square piece of paper, preferably 7 inches or larger.

STEP 1
Fold in half on the diagonal (A to A), then open and repeat (B to B), then open.

STEP 2
Fold in half—A to D and B to C, then open. Fold in half again, this time A to B and D to C, then open.

STEP 3
On existing folds, fold B, A and D to C.

New smaller square

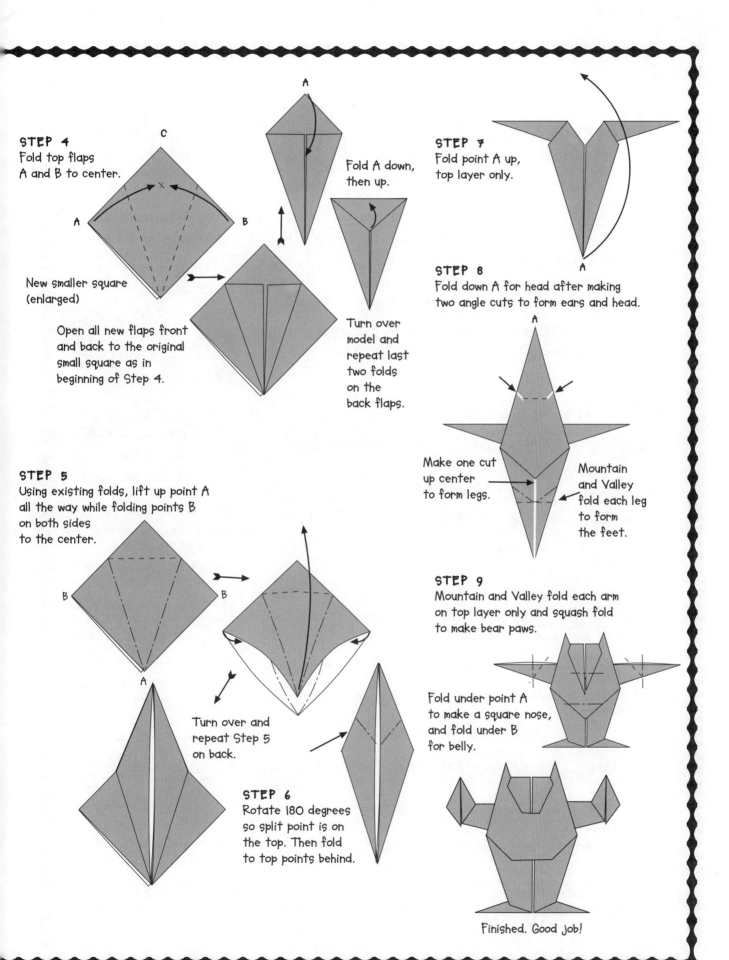

STEP 4
Fold top flaps
A and B to center.

New smaller square
(enlarged)

Open all new flaps front
and back to the original
small square as in
beginning of Step 4.

Fold A down,
then up.

Turn over
model and
repeat last
two folds
on the
back flaps.

STEP 5
Using existing folds, lift up point A
all the way while folding points B
on both sides
to the center.

Turn over and
repeat Step 5
on back.

STEP 6
Rotate 180 degrees
so split point is on
the top. Then fold
to top points behind.

STEP 7
Fold point A up,
top layer only.

STEP 8
Fold down A for head after making
two angle cuts to form ears and head.

Make one cut
up center
to form legs.

Mountain
and Valley
fold each leg
to form
the feet.

STEP 9
Mountain and Valley fold each arm
on top layer only and squash fold
to make bear paws.

Fold under point A
to make a square nose,
and fold under B
for belly.

Finished. Good job!

Fashion Do's And Don'ts

This activity works best if you have a friend, or friends, to help you. Whenever you see a blank space in the story below, ask your friend to give you an example of the type of word that we're asking for, and then write your friend's answers in the corresponding spaces. When you're done, read the completed story out loud—but try not to laugh too much!

See our definitions in box at right if you are not sure what a certain kind of word is.

You wouldn't want to wear the same _____ _____
(article of clothing)   (number)

days in a row, would you? Well, neither does your doll!

"_____! I am so tired of wearing this _____ _____
(exclamation)   (adjective)   (color)

_____ day in and day out!" said the doll. "Don't
(article of clothing)

you think I want to look _____, too?"
(adjective)

So, without another word, she put on her _____
(noun)

and _____ to _____ .
(verb, past tense)   (name of store)

"I'm _____ for a _____ that I can wear to
(verb, ending in "ing")   (noun)

_____," she told the salesperson, who just happened to be _____.
(place)   (name of person)

"_____"! We have just the thing for you! Why don't you _____ it in _____?
(Exclamation)   (verb)   (color)

It will look _____ with your _____ hair! Plus, it only costs _____ dollars!"
(adjective)   (color)   (number)

Of course, _____ was right—the doll looked _____ !
(same person you named above)   (adjective)

"This is just the beginning!" said the doll. "Next week, I'm coming back to get that

_____ _____ _____ and a pair of _____ _____
(color)   (type of material)   (noun)   (adjective)   (article of clothing, plural)

to match! I want to look just like _____!"
(name of celebrity)

DEFINITIONS

ADJECTIVE: Word that describes something or someone (fuzzy, pink, smelly)

NOUN: Person, place or thing (mouse, gas station, toy)

EXCLAMATION: A funny sound or noise ("Burp!" "Wow!")

VERB: An action word (fly, jump, blow). Past tense means it already happened (jumped, ran, shivered)

What Goes Around . . .

For the answer, count every fourth letter in the circle and write the letter in the next available space in the answer line. We've done the first one to get you on your way.

Question: What do you get when you cross a famous teddy bear with a skunk?

Answer: W_ _ _ _ _ _ _ _ _ _ _ _!

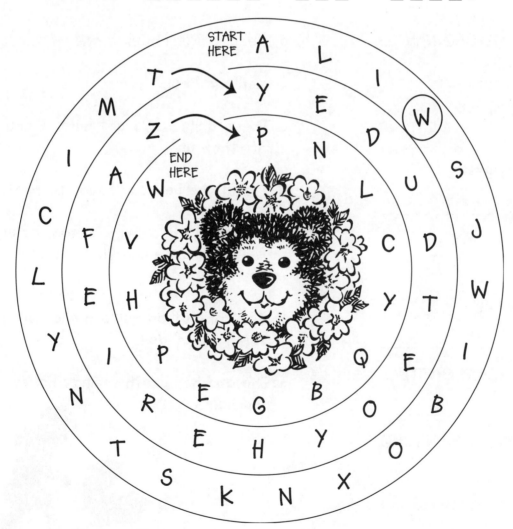

Triple-decker Teaser

Completing this puzzle is as easy (or not!) as 1, 2, 3!

1. Unscramble the words in the left-hand column.
   (Hint: They're all names of popular dolls, but you may need to use the clues in the right-hand column to figure them out.)

2. Match the unscrambled words with the correct clues in the right-hand column.

3. Find the 10 words hidden in the puzzle at right.

1. REDYGAG NAN

_____

2. EARBIB

_____

3. TUPEPP

_____

4. NIMSAY

_____

5. PAREP

_____

6. CIGAM CATTI

_____

7. RICEAMAN LIRG

_____

___ a. Felicity Merriman is one of these.

___ b. Ken's gal pal.

___ c. These dolls won't get hurt if you cut them up!

___ d. Could she be your favorite Bratz?

___ e. Where did Heather, Allison, Rosa, Megan and Keisha find the old trunk?

___ f. You can put on quite a show with this kind of doll.

___ g. She and her brother Andy have red hair.

Y P U P P E T R
N A C I R E M A
E N S F L R I G
I O A M H C D G
B A T T I C N E
R L U G S N J D
A P A Q A O X Y
B M K R E P A P

A Maze-ing Race

Help Andy find Ann as fast as you can!

START

FINISH

Riddle in the Middle

Cross out all the letters in the bears that are upside down or facing backwards.

When you're done, unscramble the letters in each bear to answer the riddle below.

(Hint: The letters in the left bear will spell out the first word of the two-word answer, and the letters in the right bear will spell out the second word.)

What do you get when you cross a pig with a teddy bear?

_____

Seeing Double

Can you find the two teddies who are exactly alike? You'll need to study them very closely to figure it out!

Clueless

You may not be "clueless," but this crossword puzzle is! Can you figure out the correct words that fit in the boxes on the grid?

P.S. Don't recognize all the words in the list? Then read up on your doll history on pages 33–36 and find out what they mean!

3-letter words
ANN
WAX

4-letter words
ANDY

5-letter words
CLOTH
PENNY
IDEAL
BRATZ

6-letter words
PADDLE
WOODEN
MADAME

7-letter words
KACHINA
CABBAGE

9-letter words
PORCELAIN
ALEXANDER

Behind the Scene

There are 29 everyday objects hidden in the scene on the opposite page.

How many can you find?

Write your answers on the lines below.

_____   _____   _____   _____

_____   _____   _____   _____

_____   _____   _____   _____

_____   _____   _____   _____

_____   _____   _____   _____

_____   _____   _____   _____

_____   _____   _____   _____

_____   _____   _____   _____

Can "Hue" Help Me?

This teddy is a bare bear! Using crayons or colored pencils, give this guy a more *colorful* personality.

B = brown
LB = light brown
DB = dark brown
BL = black
Y = yellow
R = red
G = green

What's in a Word?

How many words made up of three letters or more can you find in the words below? Take as much time as you like, and write your answers on the lines below. (FYI, people's names and proper nouns don't count.) Go for it!

P.S. Here's a clue to get you started: They say that this red fruit keeps the doctor away!

PAPER
DOLL

_____ _____

_____ _____ _____

_____ _____ _____

_____ _____ _____

_____ _____ _____

_____ _____ _____

_____ _____ _____

_____ _____ _____

_____ _____ _____

_____ _____ _____

_____ _____ _____

_____ _____ _____

_____ _____ _____

_____ _____

IF YOU FOUND...

1 to 10 words: You've made some progress, but you're "cutting" it a little close!
Give it another go.

11 to 30 words: Great job! You're a "cut" above the rest!

31 to 50 words: "Snip"-a-dee-do-da! Your genius is truly "unfolding!"

51+ words: Awesome! Stupendous! Unbelievable! We could go on and on, but you'd
probably tell us to "cut it out!"

"I," "I," Sir!

This isn't your average, everyday crossword puzzle. The words on the grid aren't numbered, so you will have to put on your thinking cap and use the clues to help you solve the puzzle. We've filled in all the "I"s for you, but you'll still need to read "Hello, Dolly" on pages 33–36 to figure out the rest.

The eight-letter word is the name of the volcano that destroyed two Italian cities in 79 A.D.

One of the four-letter words is a Native American tribe that makes kachina dolls.

People use the husks from this yellow veggie—there are four letters in its name—to make dolls.

This seven-letter word is a German word that sounds like "Dutch."

Our final four-letter word is what many fancy French dolls have on their heads.

This nine-letter word is the name of a girl who, as the story goes, froze to death.

This vertical six-letter word is the first name of the husband of Barbie's creator, Ruth Handler.

Scientists Discover World's Oldest Doll

Grab a friend—or friends—and get ready for some fun! Whenever you see a blank space in the story below, ask someone to call out an example of the type of word that we're asking for, and then write that word in the corresponding space. Be sure nobody but you can see the page, or it won't be as funny. When you're done, you can read the story out loud to everyone.

If no one else is around, you can play this game on your own, too. But just take care not to read the story until you've filled in all the blanks, or you won't laugh as much when you're done.

If you are not sure what a certain type of word is, see our definitions on the opposite page.

As reported recently by _____ , scientists from
(name of famous person)
the prestigious _____ have _____ what is
(name of school)   (verb, past tense)
believed to be the world's oldest doll. While searching
for _____ in the ancient ruins of _____ ,
(plural nouns)   (place)
Dr. _____ stumbled on a _____ piece
(repeat same famous person)   (adjective)
of _____ shaped like a human _____ .
(noun)   (part of body)

_____ immediately telephoned the talented _____ ,
(repeat same famous person)   (occupation)
_____ , well known for groundbreaking research on the _____
(name of another person)   (adjective)
_____ _____ , and asked for assistance. The two scientists began
(color)   (kind of animal)
carefully _____ around the area with a _____ . After _____ hours,
(verb ending in "ing")   (noun)   (number)
their _____ work had paid off!
(adjective)

They had found a _____ – _____ object resembling a human figure. It
_____(number)_ _(unit of measurement)_

seemed to be made of _____ and _____ , and its face was painted
_____(noun)_ _____(type of food)_

_____ . It was obviously the world's oldest doll. The doll was dressed in _____
(color) _____(color)_

_____ _____ , and also wore a _____ on its
(kind of material) _(article of clothing)_ _____(article of clothing)_

_____ . But perhaps most amazing was the doll's _____ hair, which was
(part of body) _____(color)_

_____ _____ long and very _____ .
(number) _(unit of measurement, plural)_ _____(adjective)_

The scientists carefully transported the doll by_____ to the _____
_____(type of vehicle)_ _(name of your town)_

Museum, where they determined it to be _____ years old. The doll is currently on
_____(number)_

exhibit, and its many visitors have included the famous _____ ,
_____(occupation)_

_____ , and all the members of _____ .
(name of another person) _(name of musical group)_

Admission to the exhibit is _____ dollars. To avoid the rush, it is recommended that
_____(number)_

you arrive at the museum _____ hours before it opens at _____ .
_____(number)_ _____(time of day)_

HELPFUL HINTS

ADJECTIVE: Word that describes something or
someone (fuzzy, pink, smelly)

NOUN: Person, place or thing (mouse,
gas station, toy)

EXCLAMATION: A funny sound or noise
("Burp!" "Wow!")

VERB: An action word (fly, jump, blow). Past tense
means it already happened (jumped, ran, shivered)

A or B or C?

How much do you know about dolls and bears?

Let's take a pop quiz and find out. (Relax, this one's totally fun—and it won't count on your report card!)

Read each question and select the best of the three choices that follow.

1. Who is NOT a Care Bear?
   a. Wish Bear
   b. Cher Bear
   c. Share Bear

2. What is the name of Winnie the Pooh's orange-and-black striped best bud?
   a. Tigger
   b. Tiger
   c. Tugger

3. Barbie's full name is . . .
   a. Barbie Mattel Roberts
   b. Barbara Julia Roberts
   c. Barbie Millicent Roberts

4. Yogi Bear describes himself as "smarter than the average" what?
   a. Human
   b. Rocket Scientist
   c. Bear

5. Who is NOT an American Girl?
   a. Britney Butterworth
   b. Samantha Parkington
   c. Addy Walker

6. What is the name of Barbie's little sister?
   a. Flipper
   b. Skipper
   c. Darbie

7. Who is the teddy bear named after?
   a. President Theodore Roosevelt
   b. Senator Ted Kennedy
   c. Teddy Ruxpin

8. She's a total Bratz!
   a. Diamond
   b. Jade
   c. Opal

9. What is a Raggedy Ann doll usually made of?
   a. Cloth
   b. Porcelain
   c. Wood

10. What famous entertainer had a number-one hit song called "Teddy Bear?"
    a. Justin Timberlake
    b. Madonna
    c. Elvis Presley

My Favorite Doll

Who's your best doll pal? Tell us *all* about her!

(P.S. Yes, you can have more than one favorite! You can even start your own album in a notebook or drawing pad.)

MY FAVORITE DOLL'S FULL NAME IS _____

NICKNAME(S): _____

BIRTHDAY (when your doll first came to live with you): _____

HOW MY DOLL CAME TO LIVE WITH ME: _____

_____

_____

HEIGHT: _____

HAIR COLOR: _____

EYE COLOR: _____

FAVORITE OUTFIT:_____

BESIDES ME, HER BEST FRIENDS ARE: _____

FAVORITE GAMES I PLAY WITH MY DOLL: _____

MY DOLL'S FAVORITE PLACE TO SLEEP: _____

MY DOLL'S FAVORITE PLACE TO PLAY: _____

IF I COULD GIVE MY DOLL ANYTHING IN WORLD, I'D GIVE: _____

I LOVE MY DOLL BECAUSE:_____

_____

_____

Use this space to draw a portrait of your favorite doll. You might even want to draw the both of you together.

My Favorite Bear

Time to show off your most treasured ted!

Can't decide on your number one? No problem—you can start your own album in a notebook, if you like!

MY FAVORITE BEAR'S FULL NAME IS _____

NICKNAME(S): _____

BIRTHDAY (when your bear first came to live with you): _____

HOW MY BEAR CAME TO LIVE WITH ME: _____

_____

_____

HEIGHT: _____

FUR COLOR: _____

EYE COLOR: _____

FAVORITE OUTFIT: _____

BESIDES ME, MY BEAR'S BEST BUDS ARE: _____

FAVORITE GAMES I PLAY WITH MY BEAR: _____

MY BEAR'S FAVORITE PLACE TO SLEEP: _____

MY BEAR'S FAVORITE PLACE TO PLAY: _____

IF I COULD GIVE MY BEAR ANYTHING IN WORLD, I'D GIVE: _____

I LOVE MY BEAR BECAUSE: _____

_____

_____

Here's a page to draw a picture of your favorite bear. If you want, you can draw the both of you together.

ANSWER KEY

Go'wn Around

Can you find your way out of this mess—or should we say dress?!

IN

OUT

4

WORD SEARCH
Rhyme Time

Got a few minutes to *spare*? Then grab a *chair* and give it a try—if you *dare*!
Hidden in the puzzle below are 10 words that rhyme with the word BEAR.

AIR   BEWARE   CHAIR
DARE   FAIR   HARE   PEAR
PRAYER   SPARE   TEAR

page 5

What's in a Word?

How many words of three letters or more can you find in the words Teddy Bear?
You can write your answers on the lines below. (If you run out of lines, use another sheet of paper.) People's names and proper nouns don't count. Good luck!

TEDDY BEAR

art			eat
ate			eye
bad			rat
bar			read
bare			ready
bat			rebate
bead			red
beard			tea
beat	dare	debt	tear
bed	dart	deer	trade
bee	date	drab	tray
beet	day	dread	tree
brat	dead	dye	try
bread	dear	dyed	yard
bye	debate	ear	year

IF YOU FOUND...
1 to 10 words: You're off to a good start, but you're still a cub! Keep trying, and soon you'll be ready for a hike in the forest.
11 to 30 words: Congratulations, you're on your way. Looks like they put some "smarts" in your stuffing!
31 to 50 words: Now you're really on a roll! Can we shake your paw?
51+ words: You're a rare bear indeed! Grab that jar of honey and have yourself a well-deserved reward.

page 6

Find the Twins

Can you figure out which two dolls are exactly the same?

A   B   C

D   E   F

page 7

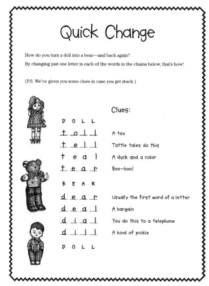

Quick Change

How do you turn a doll into a bear—and back again?
By changing just one letter in each of the words in the chains below, that's how!

(P.S. We've given you some clues in case you get stuck.)

Clues:

D O L L
t o l l   A tax
t e l l   Tattle tales do this
t e a l   A duck and a color
t e a r   Boo-hoo!
B E A R
d e a r   Usually the first word of a letter
d e a l   A bargain
d i a l   You do this to a telephone
d i l l   A kind of pickle
D O L L

page 8

Do You Remember?

Let's see how sharp your memory is!
What are your answers to the following questions?

1. What is the weather like outside?   sunny with clouds
2. What time is it?   one o'clock
3. There are two "visitors" just outside the window. Who are they?   a bird and a butterfly
4. Dolly is holding something in her right hand. What is it?   a balloon
5. What subject is Dolly studying?   math
6. What is in the cup on Dolly's desk?   a ruler and a pencil
7. What is Ted wearing?   a bowtie and a hat
8. There's something under Dolly's desk! What is it?   a football
9. Somebody's thrown an object across the room. What is it?   a paper airplane
10. What is written in Dolly's book?   MATH and 2+2=4

Bonus for brainiacs!

A. Describe the object in question #4. How is it decorated?   The balloon has stars all over it.

B. How many petals are on the flower that Ted is holding?   8 petals

page 10

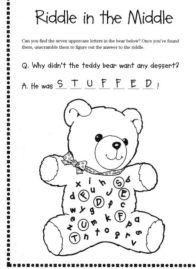

Riddle in the Middle

Can you find the seven uppercase letters in the bear below? Once you've found them, unscramble them to figure out the answer to the riddle.

Q. Why didn't the teddy bear want any dessert?

A. He was S T U F F E D !

page 11

American Girl Talk

Let's hear it for the red, white and blue!
When you complete each word in the puzzle below with the correct four-letter fragment, you'll find out about some of the popular American Girl dolls.

ARAW   ARNE   ATIV   EEDO   ERVA   EXIC
IRGI   LACK   LOTH   MOTH   NNES   ONEE   ORSE
RAID   RIDI   SCAP   TION   TRIB   VERY

Kaya is a N_ativ_e American from the Nez Perce _trib_e. She has her own horse to ride and wears her long b_lack_ hair in _raid_s.

Felicity Merriman is growing up in V_irgi_nia, just before the start of the Revolu_tion_ary War in 1776. Like Kaya, she loves _ridi_ng h_orse_s, too.

Josefina Montoya's story takes place in New M_exic_o in 1824, while **Kirsten Larson** is a pi_onee_r girl in Mi_nnes_ota in 1854. She's just arrived in America from f_araw_ay Sweden.

After e_scap_ing from slavery in 1864, **Addy Walker** and her mother have le_arne_d the true meaning of fr_eedo_m.

It's 1904, and **Samantha Parkington** lives with her rich grand_moth_er. Although she can have all the toys and c_loth_es she wants, she learns that not e_very_ little girl is as lucky. Her friend **Nellie O'Malley** works as a s_erva_nt in the house next door.

page 12

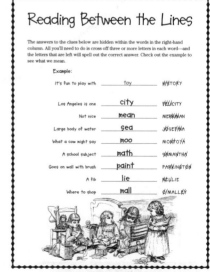

Reading Between the Lines

The answers to the clues below are hidden within the words in the right-hand column. All you'll need to do is cross off three or more letters in each word—and the letters that are left will spell out the correct answer. Check out the example to see what we mean.

Example:

It's fun to play with   toy   HiSTORY

Los Angeles is one   city   VELiCITY
Not nice   mean   MERRiMAN
Large body of water   sea   JOSEFiNA
What a cow might say   moo   MONTOYA
A school subject   math   SAMANTHA
Goes on wall with brush   paint   PARKiNGTON
A fib   lie   NELLiE
Where to shop   mall   O'MALLEY

page 13

92

page 15

Picture This

Ever **heard** of a split-level house? Well, the Berenstain **Bears** live in a split-level **tree**!

Smokey the Bear first appeared in 1944, and he is still working hard to **tell** us how to prevent forest **fires**. He always wears a brown **hat** with his name on it.

Born in **Peru**, Paddington Bear traveled to **London** when he was orphaned. He was adopted by the Brown family, and his favorite **food** is marmalade.

Winnie the Pooh's best friends are Tigger and **Piglet**. They play in the **Hundred** Acre Wood every day.

page 16

Find the Teddy Bear

Wanna play catch?

First you'll have to find your way to Teddy.

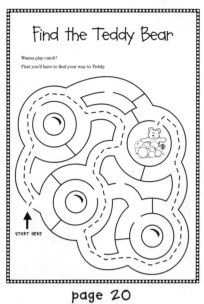

START HERE

page 20

Beary Special Spelling Bee

The capitalized words in the sentences below may sound the same, but they are spelled differently and mean different things. Put on your spelling caps and circle the words that are spelled correctly in each sentence.

A bear's claws are on his PAUSE. / PAWS.

"Swell-o, world!" says Teddy. "My NOSE / KNOWS tells me that dinner's ready!"

Name one great thing about teddies, please. Unlike dogs, they don't get FLEAS. / FLEES.

If Fuzzy Wuzzy was a BEAR, / BARE, then Fuzzy Wuzzy had no HARE / HAIR.

What happens when a grizzly growls too much? He gets HOARSE, / HORSE, of course.

Where, oh where has Teddy's tail gone? Do you think we need to GO / SEW one on?

Did you get 'em all? Good for EWE! / YOU!

page 21

Mamma Mia!

The nesting dolls you just read about are called *Matryoshka*. That term comes from the word *mater*, which is Russian for "mother." There are moms everywhere, of course, but they aren't all called "mom" everywhere! See if you can figure out what she's called in other countries by playing the matching game, below.

1. Mum — A. Spain
2. Maman — B. France
3. Mom — C. England
4. Mutter — D. United States
5. Madre — E. Germany

page 25

I Want My Mommy-or Daddy!

Teddies may not look exactly like their human buddies, but sometimes friends act and dress alike. Look at the teddies and the children below. Can you match up the teddies with their owners? (Hint: They may be wearing—or doing—something the same.) Draw a line from the bear to their Mommy—or Daddy.

page 26

Doll House Dilemma

Three girls live right next to each other in Dollywood, California, and each girl has a number-one favorite doll. Using the clues below to fill in the answer box, can you figure out where each girl lives and the name of her favorite doll?

Clues:

1. Talisha lives in the middle house.
2. April doesn't have a Swan Lake Barbie.
3. Raggedy Ann is Nicky's favorite doll.
4. One of the dolls is Polly Pocket.
5. Nicky doesn't live in the last house.

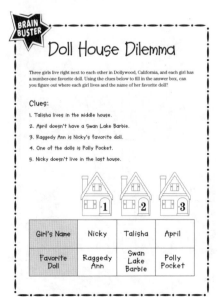

Girl's Name	Nicky	Talisha	April
Favorite Doll	Raggedy Ann	Swan Lake Barbie	Polly Pocket

page 27

Simply "D"Lightful

Study the picture at right carefully.

How many objects can you find in the scene that begin with the letter "D"? Write your answers on the lines below.

Door	Dragonfly
Doorknob	Duster
Doctor	Dust
Dog (Dachshund)	Dessert
Daisy	Dress
Derby (Hat)	Duck
Drum	Dump truck
Drumstick	Doll

page 28

Crossword solution:
SPIRIT
AMERICAN
ARIZONA
COSTUME
HARVEST
COLORFUL
UNIQUE
CLAUS

page 31

Did You Miss Me?

Barbie has had many friends and relatives over the years! Which one of her doll pals is *not* hidden in the puzzle?

MIDGE   KEN   TERESA   TUTTI

SKIPPER   STACIE   KELLY   KRISSY

```
R E P P I K S N
A   K R I S S E D
T E R E S K C   D
E G D I M F Y A
I U H Q S L G S
C X O J L S O   A
A T   P W E L V R
T     R K D Y N A T
S   E G I T T U T
```

page 32

Connect the Dots

Connect the dots and color him in!

page 49

A Rare Bear

Steiff has been making teddies for more than 100 years—and collectors are always on the lookout for the oldest and rarest bears. Steiff made some very special bears in 1912, in memory of the many people who died when a ship sank off the coast of England. You can find out more about the bear by using the clues to complete the puzzle below. You may need to refer to the story on pages 41–44 for some of the answers. (When you are done, the letters in the bold boxes will spell out the name of this famous ship.)

Clues:

1. Like all Steiff animals, this teddy has a button in his ear. Which ear?
2. The ship sunk on the 14th of this month—the 4th month in the year.
3. This special teddy is 50 cm tall. What does cm stand for?
4. Most old teddies are brown or honey-colored. But this guy's the _____ sheep of the family!
5. 600 of these special bears were sent to this city in England.
6. Kind of wool used to make Steiff teddies.
7. One of these special teddies was sold for thousands of dollars to the highest bidder at an _____

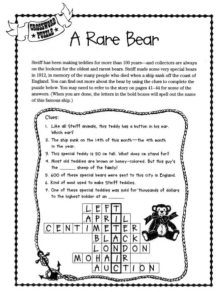

```
        L E F T
        A P R I L
C E N T I M E T E R
        B L A C K
      L O N D O N
  M O H A I R
    A U C T I O N
```

page 50

D_lls Fr_m J_p_n!

Hey, where have all the vowels gone? We need A, E, I, O and you to complete this puzzle. Use the clues to help you fill in the missing vowels in the words below while you learn about Hina Matsuri—an annual holiday in Japan when people display special dolls.

(P.S. The letters in the circles will spell out two words that describe YOU!)

S M A R T   C O O K I E

G I R L ⒮ D A Ⓨ   Until recently, this was celebrated on the same day as Hina Matsuri (Hint: Not boy's but...)

M Ⓐ R Ⓒ H   Hina Matsuri falls on the third day of this month.

A L T Ⓐ R   Japanese families display their dolls on one of these. (Hint: Spelled differently, it's what you do to clothes that don't fit.)

P E A Ⓒ H   Flower power! Blossoms from this fruit tree are traditional holiday decorations.

E M P E R Ⓞ R   Many Hina Matsuri dolls are dressed like this long-ago ruler of Japan. (Hint: There's a famous folk tale about one and his "new clothes.")

T O Ⓚ Y O   Japan's capital city

F E S T I V Ⓐ L   Time to party!

E M P R E ⓢ S   Wife of long-ago ruler of Japan

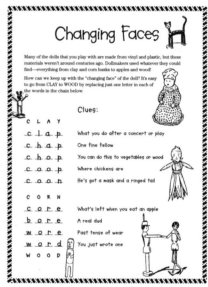

page 51

Reading Between the Lines

Now that you know the history of the teddy bear, here's your chance to really get the *inside* scoop! The answers to the clues at left are hidden within the words in the right-hand column. All you'll need to do is cross off one or more letters in each word—and the letters that are left will spell out the correct answer. Check out the example to see what we mean.

Example:

Not different ___same___   SEAMSTRESS

Not here   **there**   THEODORE

Chickens do it   **roost**   ROOSEVELT

It's sweet!   **sugar**   STUTTGART

Not black or white   **gray**   GERMANY

You'll find one onstage   **actor**   FACTORY

Bees do it   **sting**   STUFFING

Someone may send one on your birthday   **card**   RICHARD

Doesn't bend   **stiff**   STRIFF

You do this with a straw   **sip**   MISSISSIPPI

Close this to get some shut-eye   **lid**   CLIFFORD

String, jelly, or pinto   **bean**   BERRYMAN

page 52

Changing Faces

Many of the dolls that you play with are made from vinyl and plastic, but these materials weren't around centuries ago. Dollmakers used whatever they could find—everything from clay and corn husks to apples and wood!

How can we keep up with the "changing face" of the doll? It's easy to go from CLAY to WOOD by replacing just one letter in each of the words in the chain below.

Clues:

C L A Y

c l a p   What you do after a concert or play

c h a p   One fine fellow

c h o p   You can do this to vegetables or wood

c o o p   Where chickens are

c o o n   He's got a mask and a ringed tail

C O R N

c o r e   What's left when you eat an apple

b o r e   A real dud

w o r e   Past tense of wear

w o r d   You just wrote one

W O O D

page 53

A Little Bit "Mo"

You met Morris "Mo" Michtom, teddy bear maker extraordinaire, in our history of the teddy bear on pages 41–44. He and his company, the Ideal Novelty and Toy Company, made other popular toys for tots, too. To find out a little bit "mo," finish each word in the puzzle below with the correct four-letter fragment from this list.

ROOF   RITN   TTLE
ROKE   COLO   RYTH
AKAB   RAGI   NOVA   OOKE
ETSY   MOUS   TTEM
CCEE   ELAI   ESSE   EARS

Morris "Mo" Michtom loved eve**ryth**ing about teddy bears—but there was one thing he didn't like about dolls. Made of f**ragi**le porc**elai**n, they were easily b**roke**n.

What good was a doll you couldn't play with? So Mo made sure that every toy that Ideal made was unbre**akab**le.

Mo had other in**nova**tive ideas, too. He invented a doll called B**etsy** Wetsy. Guess what she did after she drank out of her bo**ttle**?!

Ideal also made dolls based on the Campbell Soup Kids. They were dr**esse**d in bright red and white, just like the **colo**rs on the soup can.

In 1934, Ideal made a doll that l**ooke**d like Shirley Temple, a child star more fa**mous** in her day than B**ritn**ey Sp**ears** is today! It took 28 a**ttem**pts to get the doll exactly right. Now there's **proof** that if at first you don't su**ccee**d, try, try again!

page 56

Picture This

Barbie has had more than **80 careers**—everything from a **rockstar** to a doctor!

The best-selling Barbie ever was **Totally** Hair **Barbie**. She had hair from her **head** to her **toes**.

Barbie's 5 sisters **are** Skipper, **Tutti**, Stacie, **Kelly**, and Krissy.

Barbie has had a **chimpanzee**, a **panda**, and a lion **cub** as pets.

page 57

```
    S T A R
    H A I R
      S I N G I N G
P I C T U R E S
    L O L L I P O P
      E Y E S
      T A P
    C H E E R
      S M I L E
    D I M P L E
    M I L L I O N
    T H R E E
```

page 59

Snack Attack

Crunchie, Munchie and Scrunchie are triplets. And like most teddies, they love sweet treats. But Mama Bear's one smart cookie! She makes her sons work for their fun! By studying the clues below to fill out the answer box, can you figure out each teddy's favorite snack—and the chore he must complete in order to get some?

Clues:

1. Munchie is allergic to strawberry Jello, but doesn't mind taking out the garbage.
2. Gummy worms are one of the bears' favorite treats.
3. One of the chores is washing the dishes.
4. Crunchie loves chocolate chip cookies.
5. Scrunchie never mows the lawn.

	Crunchie	Munchie	Scrunchie
Favorite Treat	chocolate chip cookies	gummy worms	strawberry Jello
Chore	mowing lawn	taking garbage out	washing dishes

page 60

History Mystery

Dear Aunt Sophie,

Thank you for my "bebe," as you say in France.

Her curls are like golden sunshine, and her brown eyes sparkle!

I am so lucky to have her, and I am very careful when I hold her.

I hope to sail to Europe one day, but until then,

Au Revoir!

Love,
Rebecca

page 61

Did You Miss Me?

Which famous bear from the list below *cannot* be found hidden in the puzzle?

page 65

Riddle in the Middle

You'll find all but seven letters of the alphabet in the doll's dress below. Once you've figured out which letters are missing, unscramble them to spell the name of one of the American Girl dolls.

(Hint: She's from Sweden.)

K I R S T E N

page 66

Pick a Number!

You've heard of a crossword puzzle? Well, this is more like a cross*number* puzzle! To find out the answer to the riddle, you'll first need to figure out the answers to the clues. Next, find the letter listed above #1 in the clues below and write that letter in box #1—and continue until you've filled in all 22 boxes.

What is black and white and black and white and black and white?

A PANDA ROLLING DOWN A HILL

Clues:

Not in the sea, but on ____.
L A N D
10 18 4 5

Where you rest your head in bed.
P I L L O W
2 20 21 22 8 16

Hello in Hawaii.
A L O H A
3 9 15 19 1

Another word for smile.
G R I N
13 7 11 17

What "&" stands for.
A N D
6 12 14

page 67

What Goes Around . . .

For the answer, count every fourth letter in the circle and write the letter in the next available space in the answer line. We've done the first one to get you on your way.

Question: What do you get when you cross a famous teddy bear with a skunk?

Answer: WINNIE THE PYEW!

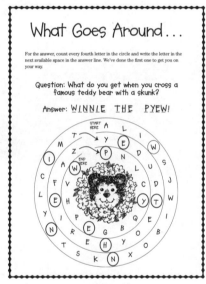

page 71

Triple-decker Teaser

Completing this puzzle is as easy (or not!) as 1, 2, 3!

1. Unscramble the words in the left-hand column.
   (Hint: They're all names of popular dolls, but you may need to use the clues in the right-hand column to figure them out.)
2. Match the unscrambled words with the correct clues in the right-hand column.
3. Find the 10 words hidden in the puzzle at right.

1. REDYGAG NAN
RAGGEDY ANN

2. EARBIB
BARBIE

3. TUPEPP
PUPPET

4. NIMGAY
YASMIN

5. PAREP
PAPER

6. CIGAM CATTI
MAGIC ATTIC

7. RICEAMAN LIRG
AMERICAN GIRL

7 a. Felicity Merriman is one of these.

2 b. Ken's gal pal.

5 c. These dolls won't get hurt if you cut them up!

4 d. Could she be your favorite Bratz?

6 e. Where did Heather, Allison, Rosa, Megan and Keisha find the old trunk?

3 f. You can put on quite a show with this kind of doll.

1 g. She and her brother Andy have red hair.

page 72

page 73

A Maze-ing Race

Help Andy find Ann as fast as you can!

page 74

Riddle in the Middle

Cross out all the letters in the bears that are upside down or facing backwards. When you're done, unscramble the letters in each bear to answer the riddle below.

(Hint: The letters in the left bear will spell out the first word of the two-word answer, and the letters in the right bear will spell out the second word.)

What do you get when you cross a pig with a teddy bear?

T E D D Y B O A R

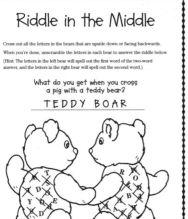

page 75

Seeing Double

Can you find the two teddies who are exactly alike? You'll need to study them very closely to figure it out!

page 76

Clueless

You may not be "clueless," but this crossword puzzle is! Can you figure out the correct words that fit in the boxes on the grid?

P.S. Don't recognize all the words in the list? Then read up on your doll history on page 33– 36 and find out what they mean!

3-letter words
ANN
WAX

4-letter words
ANDY

5-letter words
CLOTH
PENNY
IDEAL
BRATZ

6-letter words
PADDLE
WOODEN
MADAME

7-letter words
KACHINA
CABBAGE

9-letter words
PORCELAIN
ALEXANDER

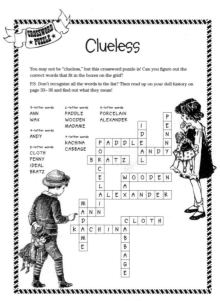

page 77

Behind the Scene

There are 29 everyday objects hidden in the scene on the opposite page.

How many can you find?
Write your answers on the lines below.

arrow	comb	iron	rabbit
balloon	envelope	knife	rocket
belt	fishing rod	mouse	scissors
bird (3)	flower pot	needle	snake
book	fork	paper	spoon
boomerang	glasses	clip	
cane	hanger	pencil	
carrot	hot dog	plane	

page 78

What's in a Word?

How many words made up of three letters or more can you find in the words below? Take as much time as you like, and write your answers on the lines below. (FYI, people's names and proper nouns don't count.) Go for it!

P.S. Here's a clue to get you started: They say that this red fruit keeps the doctor away!

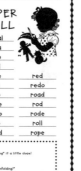

PAPER DOLL

ape	leap		
apple	load		
are	lore		
dare	oar	pedal	
deal	old	plea	
dear	older	plop	
dope	opal	pod	
dollar	pad	pole	red
drape	pal	poll	redo
drop	pale	pop	road
ear	pare	pore	rod
lap	pea	prep	rode
lard	pear	rap	roll
lead	pearl	read	rope

IF YOU FOUND...

1 to 10 words: You've made some progress, but you're "cutting" it a little close! Give it another go.

11 to 30 words: Great job! You're a "cut" above the rest!

31 to 90 words: "Snip"–a–dee–do–da! Your genius is truly "unfolding!"

91+ words: Awesome! Stupendous! Unbelievable! We could go on and on, but you'd probably tell us to "cut it out!"

page 81

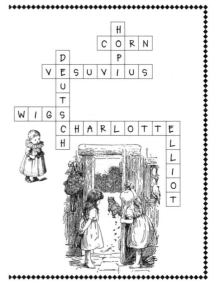

page 83

A or B or C?

How much do you know about dolls and bears?

Let's take a pop quiz and find out. (Relax, this one's totally fun—and it won't count on your report card!)

Read each question and select the best of the three choices that follow.

1. Who is NOT a Care Bear?
   a. Wish Bear
   b. Cher Bear
   c. Share Bear

2. What is the name of Winnie the Pooh's orange-and-black striped best bud?
   a. Tigger
   b. Tiger
   c. Tugger

3. Barbie's full name is...
   a. Barbie Mattel Roberts
   b. Barbara Julia Roberts
   c. Barbie Millicent Roberts

4. Yogi Bear describes himself as "smarter than the average" what?
   a. Human
   b. Rocket Scientist
   c. Bear

5. Who is NOT an American Girl?
   a. Britney Butterworth
   b. Samantha Parkington
   c. Addy Walker

6. What is the name of Barbie's little sister?
   a. Flipper
   b. Skipper
   c. Darbie

7. Who is the Teddy bear named after?
   a. President Theodore Roosevelt
   b. Senator Ted Kennedy
   c. Teddy Ruxpin

8. She's a total Bratz!
   a. Diamond
   b. Jade
   c. Opal

9. What is a Raggedy Ann doll usually made of?
   a. Cloth
   b. Porcelain
   c. Wood

10. What famous entertainer had a number-one hit song called "Teddy Bear"?
    a. Justin Timberlake
    b. Madonna
    c. Elvis Presley

page 86

page 87